# Puss in Bc

*Adapted by Alex Raynham*

## Contents

# Puss in Boots

An old miller lived with his boys, Mark, Henry and John.

John had a cat. He called it Puss.

John was a good boy, but Mark and Henry weren't good to their dad.

And they weren't good to John and Puss.

After the miller died, John cried a lot.
He loved his dad.

One day, when John was away, his brothers
left home.

They took the beds. They took all the grain.

What am I going to do?

So John gave the cat his boots and an old hat. Puss took some grain and a sack. Then he left.

Goodbye, my Puss in Boots!

Puss in Boots went into a wood.

He put some grain into the sack. Then he left it by an old tree.

Some rabbits saw the grain. They jumped into the sack.

At once, Puss in Boots closed the sack.

Puss in Boots left the wood.

He walked by fields, trees and houses.

It was a beautiful day.

Puss in Boots saw a big palace.

'Is that the palace of King Harry?' he asked.

'No, it isn't,' a man said. 'An ogre lives there, the ogre of Carabas. These are his fields, and we are afraid of him.'

'Why are you afraid of the ogre?' asked Puss in Boots.

Because he is very big!

Because he eats people!

Because he can change into an animal!

Puss in Boots had an idea.

Puss in Boots went over a river.

That night, he came to the palace of the king.

'These rabbits are a present from my lord,'
Puss in Boots told King Harry.

'I love rabbits,' said Princess Maria.
'They're beautiful.'

'Who is your lord?' asked King Harry.

'He is the Lord of Carabas,' said Puss in Boots.

'And where does he live?' asked the king.

'His palace is over the river, in Carabas,' said Puss in Boots.

Every day, Puss in Boots went to the river with some grain.

Every day, more animals jumped into his sack.

And every day, Puss in Boots took presents to the king.

'I must go to Carabas and thank your lord for all these presents,' King Harry said one day.

Puss in Boots smiled.

Go to Carabas and tell your lord 'The king is going to come tomorrow.'

Puss in Boots left the palace.

He ran over the bridge.

He ran by the fields.

That night, he came home to John.

'You must come with me to the river tomorrow,' he said.

'I don't understand,' said John.

The next day, they went to the river.

'The king wants to see you,' said Puss in Boots.

'Me?' asked John.

'Yes,' Puss in Boots said, 'But first, you must wash.'

John jumped into the river.

Puss in Boots put John's old clothes by a tree.

King Harry came in his carriage.

'Help!' cried Puss in Boots. 'Help the Lord of Carabas!'

Some men took his clothes. They left him in the river.

'Help the Lord of Carabas!' the king told his men. 'Give him new clothes.'

'Trust me, and say you are the Lord of Carabas,' Puss in Boots told John.

So John sat in the carriage with the king and Princess Maria.

He had beautiful new clothes.

Welcome, Lord Carabas.

Thank you for the presents.

Puss in Boots didn't go with John in the carriage.

He ran over the bridge, and down the road to the palace.

'The king is coming with the Lord of Carabas,' he told the people in the fields.

'Who is the Lord of Carabas?' they asked.

'He is the brother of the ogre,' said Puss in Boots.

'Welcome him home, or the ogre is going to eat you!'

'Stop the carriage at every field on the road,' the king told his men. 'I want to see Carabas.'

John smiled, and Princess Maria smiled at him.

'Welcome, King!' people in the fields cried. 'Welcome, Lord Carabas.'

The carriage stopped by houses, woods and green fields.

'Welcome home, Lord Carabas!' people cried.

'You have a lot of fields,' the king told John.

John smiled.

Puss in Boots came to the palace.

'People say you are a great ogre,' Puss in Boots said. 'But I don't believe them.'

The ogre laughed. 'Are you hungry?' he asked.

At once, there was food on the table.

'That's easy,' said Puss in Boots. 'But people say you can change into animals, too. I don't believe them.'

At once, the ogre changed into a big, hungry lion.

'Do you believe them now?' the ogre asked.

Puss in Boots was afraid, but he said, 'That is easy. A big ogre can change into a big lion. But can you change into a little mouse?'

The ogre laughed and changed into a mouse.

At once, Puss in Boots jumped on the mouse and ate it.

Then he sat and waited for the king.

'This is a nice palace for John. The king is going to like it!' thought Puss in Boots.

'Welcome to the palace of the Lord of Carabas,' Puss in Boots said when the king came.

John, the king and Princess Maria ate all the food on the table.

You have a beautiful palace. And good food!

Maria and John walked in the fields. They smiled and laughed.

'Maria is happy,' the king told John that night. 'She wants to marry you.'

John was very happy.

So, John married Princess Maria.

They lived with King Harry in his beautiful palace.

When the king died, they were the new king and queen.

Puss in Boots was the new Lord of Carabas.

He lived in the palace of Carabas.

He had beautiful clothes.

He ate beautiful food ...

... and he didn't eat a mouse again!

Clever little Puss in Boots
Can do anything.
He catches many animals
And takes them to the king.

Clever little Puss in Boots
Calls young John a lord.
The king doesn't know
That John is very poor.

Clever little Puss in Boots
Goes to the ogre's house.
He can't eat a lion
But he can eat a mouse.

Clever little Puss in Boots
Can do anything.
He becomes the Lord of Carabas
And John becomes the king.

# Word list

| | | | | |
|---|---|---|---|---|
| a | closed | home | no | thank you |
| afraid | clothes | houses | now | that |
| after | coming | how | of | the |
| a lot of | cried | hungry | ogre | then |
| all | dad | I | old | they |
| am | day | idea | one | three |
| an | died | into | or | there/there's |
| and | didn't | is/isn't | over | these |
| animal | do/does/don't | it | palace | they |
| asked | down | jumped | people | to |
| at | easy | king | present | too |
| at once | eat | laughed | princess | took |
| ate | every | left | put | tree |
| back | fields | lion | queen | trust |
| be | first | little | rabbits | understand |
| beautiful | food | lived | ran | very |
| because | from | lord | road | waited |
| beds | give/gave | love/loved | smiled | walked |
| believe | go/went | man | sack | wanted |
| big | going to | marry/married | sat | was |
| bridge | good | me | see/saw | wash |
| brother | grain | men | say/said | weren't |
| but | great | miller | so | what |
| by | green | more | some | with |
| can | have/has/had | mouse | stop/ | who |
| cat | hat | must | stopped | why |
| called | he | my | table | wood |
| came | him | new | take | you |
| carriage | his | next | tell/told | your |
| change/changed | help | night | thank | |

# Language structures

## Imperatives

Help the Lord of Carabas.
Give him new clothes.
Stop the carriage at every field on the road.

## Past simple

John had a cat. He called it Puss.
Maria and John walked in the fields. They smiled and laughed.

## Adjectives

An old miller lived with his three boys.
Puss in Boots was afraid.

## Prepositions of movement

He ran over the bridge, and down the road to the palace.

## *Going to*

Now I'm going to take these rabbits to King Harry.
Welcome him home, or the ogre is going to eat you!

## *There was*

At once, there was food on the table.

## *Must*

I must have your boots, and some grain.
I must go to Carabas and thank your lord for all these presents.

## *Can*

How can a little cat help me?
Trust me. I can help you.

## Quantifiers

He put some grain into the sack.
You have a lot of fields.